RUSSIA

**Written by
Merle Davenport**

Cover Design
by
Matthew Van Zomeren

Inside Illustrations
by
Don Ellens

Publishers
Instructional Fair • TS Denison
Grand Rapids, Michigan 49544

Permission to Reproduce

About the Author

Merle Davenport holds a Bachelor of Arts Degree from Spring Arbor College with a major in history and a minor in social studies. He received his teaching certification through Olivet College.

Credits

Author: Merle Davenport
Cover Design: Matthew Van Zomeren
Inside Illustrations: Don Ellens
Project Director: Rhonda DeWaard
Editors: Lisa Hancock, Ruth Gray
Typesetting/Layout: Pat Geasler

Cover Photograph: © Corel Corporation

Standard Book Number: 1-56822-445-1
Living Geography—Russia
Copyright © 1998 by Instructional Fair • TS Denison
2400 Turner Avenue NW
Grand Rapids, Michigan 49544

Table of Contents

Introduction

This book is intended to raise our awareness of both the plight of the Siberian Tiger and the land in which it lives. It touches on history, geography, literature, and other elements of life in Russia. It links environmental issues, especially the fast-disappearing Siberian Tiger, with the human cultures that share that environment.

The plight of the tiger around the world is serious. Around the turn of the century, about 100,000 tigers existed in the wild. Today, there are less than 5,000.

Of the eight subspecies of tigers, three are already extinct. The Bali Tiger became extinct in the 1940s, the Caspian Tiger became extinct in the 1970s, and the Javan Tiger became extinct in the 1980s. In the 1950s, the South China Tiger was hunted almost to extinction. Today, there are 30–80 left in the wild. The Siberian Tiger is the largest of these regal cats. However, less than 200 are left in the Taiga Forest. Even the Bengal Tiger of India is in danger. There are currently 3,300–4,500 living in India, but the tremendous increase in human population has placed impossible demands on their habitat.

Although loss of habitat is a major reason for the demise of the tiger, the primary cause is poaching. Many residents of Taiwan, China, and Korea believe in the healing properties of various parts of the tiger. Pills are made from the various parts to cure everything from rheumatism to convulsions. Tiger bone potions are even supposed to increase longevity. Also, a tiger skin can fetch as much as $15,000 on the black market. After the dissolution of the Soviet Union, borders opened and foreign trade increased.

In 1994, President Clinton imposed limited sanctions on Taiwan in response to its lack of effort in stopping the market for tiger parts. China narrowly escaped similar action.

Another threat to the tiger is logging. Logging companies clear-cut trees, leaving no homes for tigers or other forest animals.

Ultimately, the tiger will disappear from the face of the planet. The sad truth is that if we do not save the tiger now, the other great cats of the world, like the lion and panther, may also disappear.

Physical Features of Russia

Russia is the largest country in the world. It encompasses most of Eastern Europe and all of Northern Asia. Thousands of lakes and rivers run through this vast land.

Identify the following features by writing the correct number in each blank.

___ Aral Sea	___ Sea of Japan	___ Volga River	___ Caucasus Mtns.
___ Caspian Sea	___ Sea of Okhotsk	___ Yenisey River	___ Arctic Circle
___ Barents Sea	___ Lake Ladoga	___ Ob River	___ Sakhalin Island
___ Black Sea	___ Lake Baikal	___ Lena River	___ Kuril Islands
___ White Sea	___ Gulf of Finland	___ Amur River	
___ Bering Sea	___ Bering Strait	___ Ural Mtns.	
___ Sea of Azov	___ Dnepr River		

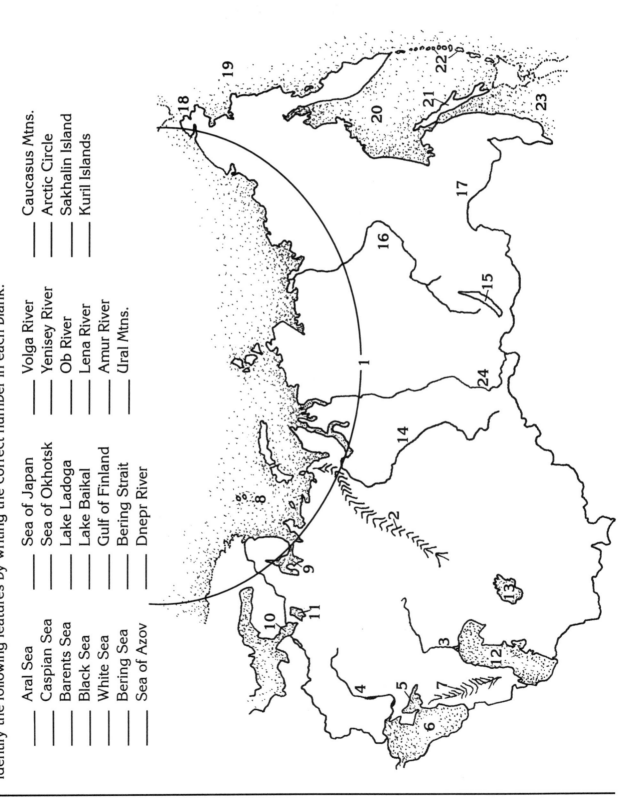

Use with page 7.

Russia and Its Neighbors

Fill in the names of the countries and independent states in the word puzzle below. Not all the names will be included. Then, on the map on page 7, write all the names from the Word Bank on the map.

Word Bank

Japan	Iran	Finland
Turkey	Sweden	Mongolia
Poland	China	Armenia
Kazakstan	Kyrgyzstan	Lithuania
Uzbekistan	Turkmenistan	Russia
Azerbaijan	Georgia	Latvia
Ukraine	Belarus	Estonia

1. __ __ e __ __ n
2. __ __ __ n __
3. __ __ l a __ __ __
4. __ e __ g __ __
5. __ a __ a n
6. __ u __ __ __ __
7. __ __ b __ __ i __ __ __ __
8. __ k __ __ i __ __
9. __ a t __ i __
10. __ s __ __ n __ __
11. __ r __ __
12. __ __ r __ m __ __ __ s __ __ __
13. __ y __ g __ __ __ t __ __
14. __ __ l __ n __
15. __ __ z __ k __ __ __ __
16. __ u __ s __ __

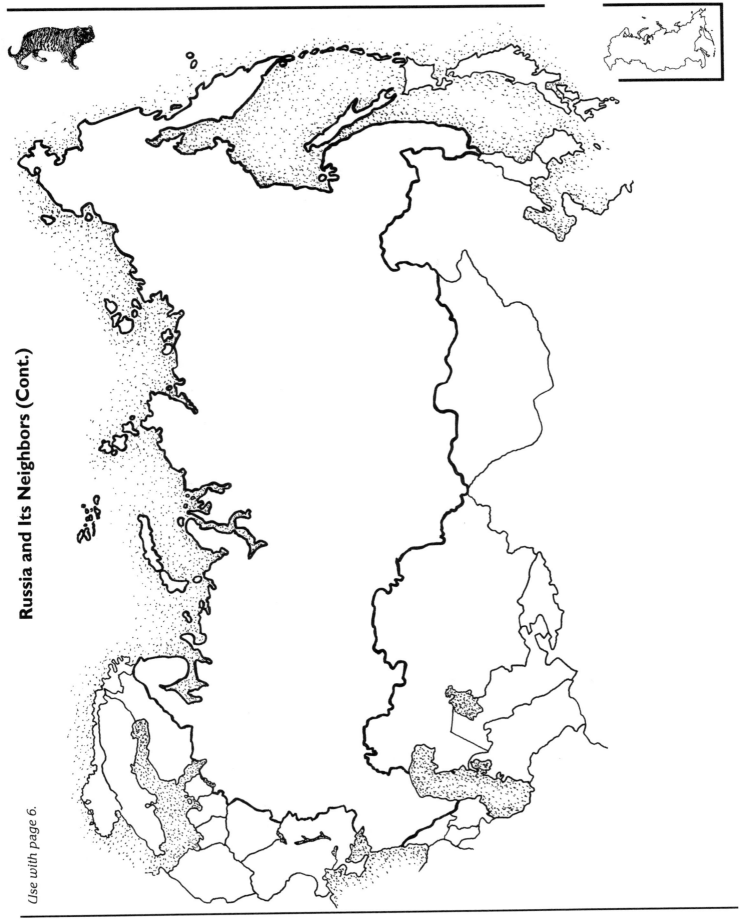

Russia and Its Neighbors (Cont.)

Use with page 6.

How Big Is Russia?

Russia = 6,593,000 sq. miles
Former Soviet Union = 8,649,000 sq. miles
United States = 3,619,000 sq. miles
Germany = 138,000 sq. miles
France = 213,000 sq. miles
China = 3,696,000 sq. miles
India = 1,269,000 sq. miles
Canada = 3,850,000 sq. miles

Asia = 16,992,000 sq. miles
Europe = 4,033,000 sq. miles
Africa = 11,681,000 sq. miles
Australia = 2,978,000 sq. miles
North America = 9,348,000 sq. miles
South America = 6,885,000 sq. miles
Antarctica = 5,400,000 sq. miles

Refer to the size of each country, as listed above, to answer these questions.

1. What percentage of the former Soviet Union was Russia? _____

2. What percentage of Russia is the United States? _____

3. What percentage of Russia is China? _____

4. What percentage of Asia is Russia? _____

5. What percentage of Russia is Europe? _____

6. What percentage of Africa is Russia? _____

7. What percentage of Russia is Australia? _____

8. What percentage of North America is Russia? _____

9. What percentage of South America is Russia? _____

10. What percentage of Russia is Antarctica? _____

11. What percentage of Russia is your country? _____

Time Zones

Below is a map of the time zones in Russia. Study it and answer these questions.

1. If it is 12:00 Noon in Moscow, what time is it in each city?

   Yekaterinburg _____ Novosibirsk _____ Yakutsk _____

2. How would the varying time zones affect doing business in Russia?

   _____

   _____

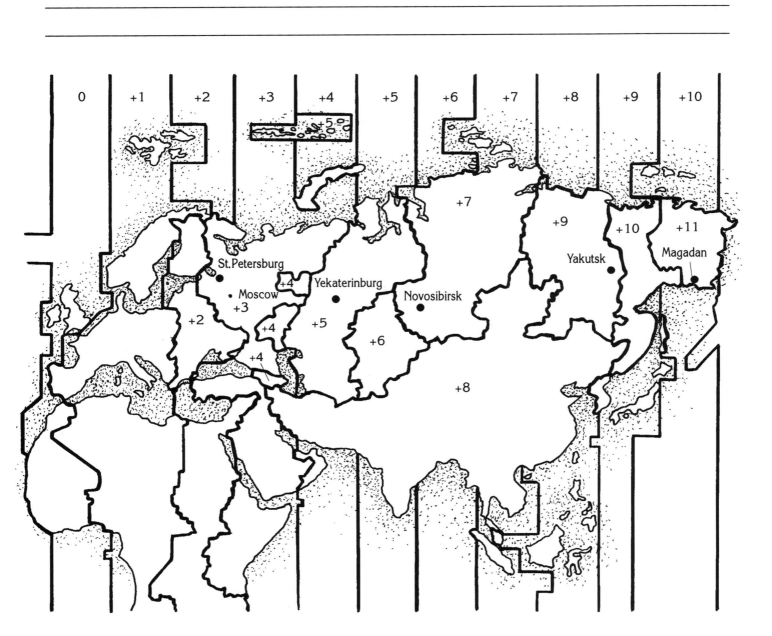

The Kremlin

Beside the Moscow River stands a fortress known as the Kremlin. Actually, *kremlin* simply means a fortified place. But in Moscow, the Kremlin is the nerve center for all of Russia. Below is a map of the Kremlin. Compare it to a map of Washington, D.C., mall area. How are they alike, and how are they different?

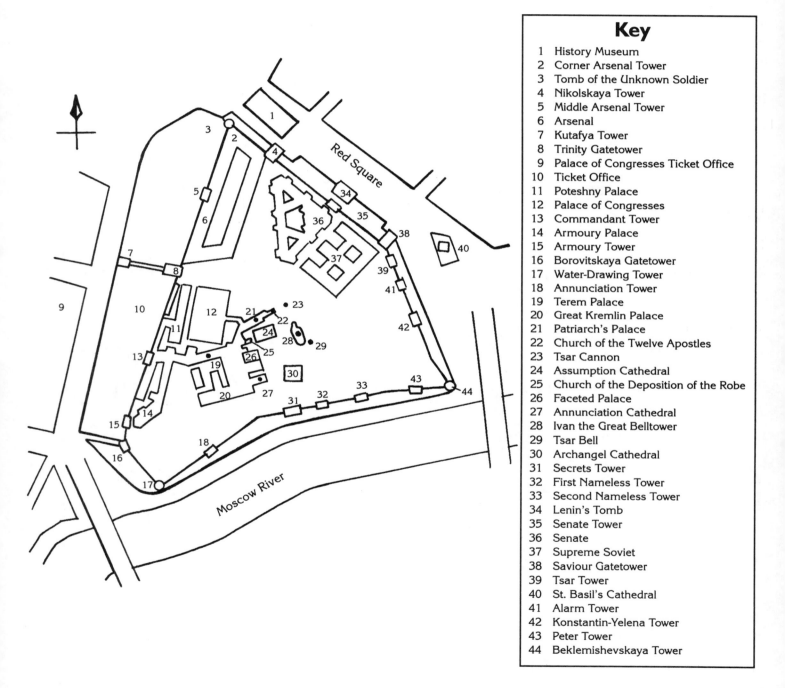

Key

1	History Museum
2	Corner Arsenal Tower
3	Tomb of the Unknown Soldier
4	Nikolskaya Tower
5	Middle Arsenal Tower
6	Arsenal
7	Kutafya Tower
8	Trinity Gatetower
9	Palace of Congresses Ticket Office
10	Ticket Office
11	Poteshny Palace
12	Palace of Congresses
13	Commandant Tower
14	Armoury Palace
15	Armoury Tower
16	Borovitskaya Gatetower
17	Water-Drawing Tower
18	Annunciation Tower
19	Terem Palace
20	Great Kremlin Palace
21	Patriarch's Palace
22	Church of the Twelve Apostles
23	Tsar Cannon
24	Assumption Cathedral
25	Church of the Deposition of the Robe
26	Faceted Palace
27	Annunciation Cathedral
28	Ivan the Great Belltower
29	Tsar Bell
30	Archangel Cathedral
31	Secrets Tower
32	First Nameless Tower
33	Second Nameless Tower
34	Lenin's Tomb
35	Senate Tower
36	Senate
37	Supreme Soviet
38	Saviour Gatetower
39	Tsar Tower
40	St. Basil's Cathedral
41	Alarm Tower
42	Konstantin-Yelena Tower
43	Peter Tower
44	Beklemishevskaya Tower

Build Your Own St. Basil's Cathedral

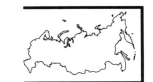

St. Basil's Cathedral is perhaps Russia's most recognized symbol. St. Basil the Blessed was a barefoot holy man who lived during the reign of Ivan the Terrible. He predicted Ivan's victory over the Tartars at Kazan. He also foretold that Ivan would murder his own son. While Ivan was away fighting the Tartars, St. Basil died and was buried beside the church.

Ivan built St. Basil's Cathedral in the 1550s. The richly patterned onion-shaped domes were added in the 1670s.

Follow the directions below to make your own model of St. Basil's Cathedral.

Materials:

scissors
toilet and paper towel tubes
cardboard or construction paper

glue (or stapler)
colored paper
crayons or colored pencils

Directions:

1. Cut four strips of construction paper (1" x 8") for each dome.

2. Arrange strips in a criss-cross pattern and glue (or staple) in the center.

3. Fold up the ends and glue (or staple) at the top.

4. Cover tubes of various heights with colored paper.

5. Place onion domes on the tubes.

6. Place Russian crosses on top of the domes.

7. Use construction paper to fill in the other details of the cathedral.

8. Color your cathedral with crayons or colored pencils.

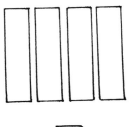

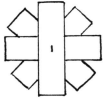

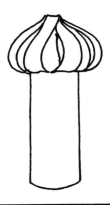

Use with page 13.

Chronology of Events

A.D. 830	The "Rus" begin to leave Scandinavia and settle in Russia
862	Rurik, a Viking, becomes the first ruler of Novgorod
988	Vladimir converts to Christianity and establishes it as the state religion
1223	First Mongol raid against the Rus
1237–1242	Mongols conquer Russia
1242	Nevsky destroys the German Teutonic Knights by leading them onto Lake Piepus until the ice breaks
1328	Ivan I (Moneybags) becomes grand prince of Moscow
1480	Ivan III ends payment of tribute to Mongols
1547–1584	Reign of Ivan IV ("The Terrible")
1547–1556	Ivan adopts the title of *tsar* from the Latin *Caesar*
1552	Ivan conquers Kazan and Astrakhan, expanding the Russian empire
1558	Ivan authorizes the Stroganov family to open Siberia for trade (Russia's equivalent of America's Wild West)
1565–1572	Period of Ivan's "Reign of Terror"
1571	Crimean Tartars raid Moscow
1605–1606	The False Dmitri reigns
1610	Poles rule Moscow
1612	Poles driven out of Moscow
1613	Michael Romanov becomes Czar
1649	Serfdom becomes a legal institution
1689–1725	Reign of Peter I (The Great)
1697	Peter tours Europe to modernize Russia
1712	Peter moves capital from Moscow to St. Petersburg
1735–1739	One of many Russo-Turkish wars
1742	Vitus Bering lands in Alaska
1762–1796	Reign of Catherine II (the Great) after the murder of Peter III
1770–1779	Catherine encourages the arts and education among the privileged
1772	First Partition of Poland
1775	Catherine tightens landowners' control over serfs
1783	Russian Annexation of Crimea
1801–1825	Reign of Alexander I
1805	Battle of Austerlitz against Napoleon
1812	Napoleon invades Russia with 600,000 men of the Grande Army; Russians fight French off in severe winter after they take Moscow; French retreat; Napoleon arrives in Paris with fewer than 10,000 men
1815	Napoleon defeated at the Battle of Waterloo
1823	Monroe Doctrine established partly to prevent Russian involvement in North America
1853–1856	Crimean War against France, Britain, and the Ottoman Empire
1854	Charge of the British Light Brigade at the Battle of Balaklava
1861	Serfs are officially emancipated

Chronology of Events (Cont.)

Use with page 12.

A.D. 1867 — Alaska sold to the U.S. for $7.2 million

1869 — Tolstoy finishes writing *War and Peace*

1899 — Trans-Siberian Railway completed, stretching over 4,500 miles

1904 — Beginning of Russo-Japanese War

1905 — Revolution of 1905; "Bloody Sunday" in St. Petersburg where government troops kill hundreds of marching workers

1914 — World War I begins

1917 — Abdication of Czar Nicolas II. Bolsheviks seize power in the October Revolution

1918 — Murder of Romanovs, the last Czar family

1922 — The U.S.S.R. is formed under Lenin

1924 — Death of Lenin

1929–1953 — Rule of Stalin

1931–1939 — Purges of former Left Bolsheviks, army, and Right Bolsheviks

1939 — Nazi-Soviet pact nonaggression

1941 — Nazi Germany attacks U.S.S.R.

1943 — German advance stopped at Stalingrad

1945 — End of World War II; establishment of Eastern Europe under Communist rule

1949 — U.S.S.R. explodes its first atomic bomb

1957 — Sputnik launched

1960 — Gary Powers shot down over U.S.S.R.

1961 — Yuri Gagarin is the first man in space

1962 — Cuban Missile Crisis

1968 — Red Army crushes "Prague Spring"

1978 — KGB suppresses attempts by workers to form independent unions

1979 — Soviet invasion of Afghanistan

1985 — Gorbachev seizes power; introduction of *glasnost* and *perestroika*

1986 — Chernobyl nuclear meltdown

1989 — Fall of Berlin Wall

1991 — Communist coup attempt to regain Moscow fails; Yeltsin elected president

1992 — Russian Federation Treaty signed by 19 autonomous states

1995 — War with the Chechens

—— **Activity** ——

Make a timeline with illustrations showing several major events in Russia's history. Also, use these pages with "Library Research" (page 14).

Library Research

Russia is home to many significant events. Look over the *Chronology of Events* (pages 12 and 13) and select one you want to know more about. Then go to the library to find more information. Sources may include encyclopedias, *National Geographic*, magazines, history books, newspapers, and biographies. Ask your librarian for help.

Gather your information and keep notes on this page about what you learned. Then write a report.

Event: _____

When it happened: _____

Who was involved: _____

_____

What happened: _____

_____

_____

_____

Results of event: _____

_____

_____

_____

_____

1812

Napoleon's invasion of Russia in 1812 marks one of the most significant events in world history. Napoleon was master of Europe. He had defeated all opponents in battle and conquered everything from the western edge of Spain, to the southern tip of Italy, to the eastern border of Poland.

With 600,000 men, Napoleon invaded Russia. The tactic of the Russian army was to retreat, burning everything as they went. This forced the French to live off their supplies, making it impossible for them to forage for food. The French then occupied Moscow itself as the Russians evacuated Moscow and released all their prisoners with orders to burn down Moscow around the French.

With Moscow in flames, the French retreated to France. The Cossacks harassed their supply lines so effectively that thousands died of exposure and starvation. By the time Napoleon arrived in Paris, he had fewer than 10,000 men left from his Grande Army.

This marked the turning point in Napoleon's military career. The other powers of Europe united to engineer his final defeat at the Battle of Waterloo in 1815.

The Invasion of 1812 is a source of great pride for Russia. It has been commemorated in literature and song. Leo Tolstoy's massive work, *War and Peace*, covers the Napoleonic wars with a cast of thousands of characters. Peter Tchaikovsky wrote the *1812 Overture* to celebrate the victory in music.

—— **Activity** ——

Obtain a recording of Tchaikovsky's *1812 Overture*. Read the events of the French invasion of Russia. Then play the overture and identify the events through the music. Note the Russian Hymn, the French national anthem, the cannons, and the bells of victory.

Siberian Labor Camps

Beginning around 1650, The Russian government began sending criminals to Siberia to work in labor camps. Exiles were put to work harvesting Siberia's enormous mineral wealth. The list of offenses increased so more could be sent to work in the camps. Even the death penalty was abolished to expand forced labor in Siberia. By 1890, around 3,400 exiles per week were marched into the camps. Much of the Trans-Siberian Railroad was built by "criminals."

The exile system was abolished around 1900. However, Joseph Stalin reinstituted it on a grand scale in the 1930s. It was expanded into a sort of slave trade. In a combination of resettlement programs, transit prisons, labor colonies, concentration camps, and special psychiatric hospitals, the GULAG (an acronym that stands for the Soviet penal system and its administration) flourished. The inmates, whose so-called crimes were often simply being Jewish, an artist, or an acquaintance of a dissident, dug canals, cut trees, and built roads.

—— **Activity** ——

Compare how Russia has changed since 1985, when Gorbachev took power. Talk about personal, political, and religious freedom. Also discuss the role of prisons in society. How should they be designed? What is their purpose?

Trans-Siberian Railroad

The Trans-Siberian Railroad was one of the greatest engineering feats of this century. Completed in 1899, it stretched about 8,000 kilometers from Sverdlovsk to Vladivostok. Builders had to cross steep mountains, swamps, tundra, and even a lake. Dozens of tunnels and over 200 bridges and viaducts were completed for the railroad around the southern end of the lake. During World War I (1914–1918) and World War II (1939–1945), the railroad was used to move troops and supplies.

Before the railroad was built, the only way to travel in Siberia was by river. Although Siberia has thousands of rivers, most of them run north and south and are frozen for much of the year. Even the Arctic Ocean, which is frozen for much of the year, was not passable. The railroad made it possible to move people and goods into Siberia and raw materials out of Siberia.

Much of the land through which the railroad ran is "tundra," a great, cold desert. It consists of a frozen bog, called permafrost, that can be several hundred yards deep. The weight and warmth of a railroad track can turn the tundra to mud and sink the track. So one of the challenges of building a railroad (or any structure) is to put enough insulation under the railroad to keep it from throwing heat.

To get an idea of the length of the railroad, imagine riding on a train nonstop from Sverdlovsk in the west to Vladivostok on the east coast. It will take seven days to make the trip!

No railroad today is officially called the Trans-Siberian Railroad. It has been joined to other railroads in the region.

1. When trying to settle new territory, how important is reliable transportation?

   _____

2. In what ways would your life change if your only means of transportation were your feet?

   _____

3. What would you be able to buy in a store if nothing could be brought in from other places?

   _____

4. The Trans-Siberian Railroad is about 8,000 km long. How many miles is it? _____

5. About how many kilometers per hour would a train travel if it took seven days to travel 8,000 km?

   _____

6. List the names of two cities about 8,000 km from your school. _____

   _____

7. Compare the Trans-Siberian Railroad to the Union Pacific Railroad, which spans the American West.

   _____

   _____

World War II

In 1939, Hitler invaded Poland. This marked the beginning of World War II. Initially, Russia was allied with Germany and Japan. However, in 1941, Hitler invaded Russia. The Germans advanced until they were stalled at Stalingrad. The Soviet resistance was so stubborn that the Germans were held up for five months until the Red Army arrived to stem the tide of the German advance. By 1945, the Soviets and the Allies captured Berlin and ended Germany's bid for power.

After the war, Europe fell under two spheres of influence. Western Germany, Austria, and Italy were under the Allied protection of NATO (North Atlantic Treaty Organization) while East Germany, Czechoslovakia, Poland, Hungary, Yugoslavia, Romania, and Bulgaria (Eastern Bloc countries or Warsaw Pact) fell under the influence of the Soviet Union. In general, Eastern Europe had communist governments and Western Europe had democratic governments. The line that divided Europe was known as the Iron Curtain.

European Civilians Killed in WWII	
Jews	6,000,000
Russians	3,000,000
Yugoslavs	1,280,000
Polish	1,000,000
Germans	800,000
Hungarians	280,000
Romanians	260,000
Dutch	200,000
Greeks	140,000
French	107,000
Austrians	104,000
British	62,000
Belgians	16,000
Total	Over 13 million

Soldiers Killed in WWII	
Russians	7,500,000
Germans	3,500,000
Hungarians	410,000
Yugoslavs	410,000
British	400,000
Italians	330,000
Polish	320,000
Romanians	300,000
Americans	290,000
French	210,000
Finns	85,000
Belgians	12,000
Dutch	12,000
Total	Over 13 million

Compare the cost in human lives of World War II to the cost in lives of living in the Soviet Union under Stalin, 1929–1953. Figures are from the KGB files released in 1991.

Lost Lives Under Stalin 1929–1953	
Killed in purges of the army and civilians	27 million
Killed in Siberian Labor Camps	15 million
Total	Over 42 million

Chernobyl, A Nuclear Accident

The sequence of events listed below tell the story of the disaster at Chernobyl in 1986. Write a story from the perspective of an engineer who is witnessing these steps happening. Or write a newspaper article detailing the disaster.

1. The nuclear power plant at Chernobyl was designed so that the emergency cooling system had to be turned off to run a safety test.

2. During the test, the nuclear reaction began to slow down.

3. The safety rods of the regular cooling system were removed to increase the power.

4. The reaction overheated and coolant boiled out of the reactor pipes.

5. The reactor became seriously unstable.

6. To slow down the reactor, the safety rods were lowered back in place.

7. The first three feet of the safety rods are hollow, so they caused a power surge when they were lowered into the core.

8. The power surge caused steam explosions which ripped apart the pipes in the regular cooling system.

9. Hydrogen and oxygen gases built up inside the reactor.

10. When the gases exploded, the top of the safety shield was blown off and a hole through the roof of the power plant was created.

11. Fifty tons of radioactive materials were thrown into the atmosphere.

12. A radioactive cloud spread over most of Europe.

13. The nuclear core melted through the lower radiation shield and through the bottom of the power plant.

14. The highly radioactive material continued to burn and throw radiation into the air until it finally cooled on its own.

15. Over 10,000 people were killed by the radiation.

16. The topsoil for miles around became radioactive and dangerous for growing crops.

17. Thousands of cattle and animals were killed or contaminated by the radiation.

18. Thousands of people got radiation sickness. Adults became sterile, and children demonstrated a wide variety of disabilities.

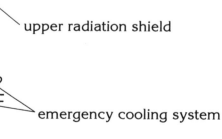

safety rods

coolant pipes

reactor core

upper radiation shield

emergency cooling system

ON OFF

The Break-Up and Beyond

Few people thought they would live to see the day when the giant Communist nation known as the Soviet Union would cease to exist. Yet that is exactly what happened in recent history. The struggle of the 15 Soviet republics for independence can be traced back to 1985 when Mikhail Gorbachev became head of the Communist Party. Gorbachev is known for instituting *glasnost, or "openness,"* an official policy emphasizing freedom of expression in the arts and the frank discussion of shortcomings of the Soviet system. Gorbachev also encouraged economic reforms including greater self-management and decreased controls on prices and profits.

The push for independence increased momentum in the late 1980s when people from all over the Soviet Union (U.S.S.R) pressed for more freedom from the central government. In June 1990, Russia, the largest of the 15 Soviet republics, declared that its laws transcended the laws of the Soviet Union. Within six months all of the other republics followed suit. In July 1991, after Gorbachev signed treaties increasing self-government for ten republics, Communist hard-liners led a coup, attempting to halt the reforms and return to strict Communist order. Gorbachev could not fight the coup; he and his family were imprisoned in their vacation home. However, Boris Yeltsin, the popular president of the Russian republic, managed to fight and defeat the coup.

Gorbachev was reinstated as president of an interim government, but the collapse of the coup produced an unstoppable demand for self-government. By the end of 1991, Yeltsin, with the presidents of Belarus and Ukraine, formed the Commonwealth of Independent States (C.I.S.), and proclaimed the end of the U.S.S.R. Yeltsin took over the central government of the Soviet Union, including the Kremlin, and on December 25, 1991, Gorbachev resigned as the Soviet president. The Soviet Union officially ceased to exist.

An immediate effect of the break-up was the end of the Cold War between the Soviet Union and the U.S. The two superpowers, who for over four decades watched each other with wary suspicion, could now divert their tremendous resources from military build-up to civilian projects. The shifting focus in resources and power was not without difficulties. Within the former U.S.S.R., the great number of military workers had to find jobs in a difficult civilian economy. As East Bloc countries (such as the former Czechoslovakia and Yugoslavia) outside of the U.S.S. R. gained independence, groups within these countries pressed to form their own smaller countries. The bloody struggle taking place through much of the 1990s between Bosnians, Serbs, and Croats in the former Yugoslavia left millions dead; this war may not have taken place had iron-fisted Soviet order been in place.

Many Russians saw a decline in their standard of living as the removal of government controls caused prices to skyrocket. In December 1993 Vladimir Zhirinovsky gained great support against Yeltsin in the election for president. Yeltsin won, but Zhirinovsky, who wants to do away with recent economic reforms and believes Russia should take control of the former republics, maintains a following. The standard of living has improved for some, and Moscow, the capital of Russia, is the beneficiary of projects unheard of during Communist days. These include the construction of a colossal cathedral and also a showy shopping mall erected just outside the Kremlin.

The Break-Up and Beyond (Cont.)

Answer these questions after reading the article on page 20.

1. Who are Communist hard-liners and how did Gorbachev come to power with them in control?

   _____

   _____

2. Why do you think Yeltsin became president of the new Russia and not Gorbachev?

   _____

   _____

3. Do you agree that conflict in Eastern Europe may not have occurred had the Soviet Union maintained control of East Bloc countries? Explain.

   _____

   _____

4. Why do you think someone like Zhirinovsky has political appeal? _____

   _____

5. Do you think a large shopping mall in the heart of Moscow represents an improvement? Explain.

   _____

Cyrillic Alphabet

In the 9th century, the Eastern Orthodox church based in Constantinople sent two missionaries to the Slavic people. Saint Cyril worked among the Slavs on the north side of the Black Sea. They had no written language, so he listened to the various sounds of their speech and created an alphabet based on Greek letters. He was then able to translate the Bible into their language. Saint Methodius revised the alphabet to make it easier to learn.

Look at the modern Cyrillic alphabet below. Note how the 33 symbols represent sounds or combinations of sounds. Listen to the sounds of your name and write it using the Cyrillic alphabet. Write other words in Cyrillic and see if your friends can read what you have written.

Letter	Transliteration	Letter	Transliteration
А, а	A, a	Р, р	R, r
Б, б	B, b	С, с	S, s
В, в	V, v	Т, т	T, t
Г, г	G, g	У, у	U, u
Д, д	D, d	Ф, ф	F, f
Е, е	Ye, e	Х, х	Kh, kh
Ё, ё	Yo, yo	Ц, ц	Ts, ts
Ж, ж	Zh, zh	Ч, ч	Ch, ch
З, з	Z, z	Ш, ш	Sh, sh
И, и	I, i	Щ, щ	Shch, shch
Й, й	Y, y	ъ	(no symbol)
К, к	K, k	Ы, ы	Y, y
Л, л	L, l	ь	(no symbol)
М, м	M, m	Э, э	E, e
Н, н	N, n	Ю, ю	Yu, yu
О, о	O, o	Я, я	Ya, ya
П, п	P, p		

Words and Phrases

English	Russian	Cyrillic	English	Russian	Cyrillic
they	ANI	ОНИ	**shop/store**	muh-guh-ZYIN	магазин
good bye	das-fi-DA-nya	До свидания.	**open**	aht-KRIT	открыт
thank you	spuh-SEE-ba	Спасибо	**closed**	zuh-KRIT	закрыт
good	kha-ra-SHOH	хорошо	**please**	pa-kuh-ZHEE-tyeh	Покажите
bad	PLOH-kha	плохо	**help**	na POH-mushch	На помощь
bus	uf-TOH-boos	автобус	**when**	kahg-DA	когда
taxi	tahk-SEE	такси	**today**	si-VOHD-nyuh	сегодня
building	KOR-poos	корпус	**yesterday**	fchi-RA	вчера
theater	ti-ATR	театр	**tomorrow**	ZAHF-truh	завтра
circus	tsirk	цирк	**1**	ah-DYIN	один
north	SYEH-vir	север	**2**	dva	два
south	yook	юг	**3**	tree	три
east	va-STOK	восток	**4**	chi-TIR-yeh	четыре
west	ZAH-puht	запап	**5**	pyaht	пять
here	toot	тут	**6**	shest	шесть
there	tahm	там	**7**	syem	семь
I'm lost	ya zuh-blu-DEEL-suh	Я заблудился	**8**	VO-syim	восемь
breakfast	ZAHF-truk	завтрак	**9**	DYEV-yut	девять
lunch	a-BYET	обед	**10**	DYES-yut	десять
supper	OO-zhin	ужин	**100**	stoh	сто

Crossword Puzzle

Write the English words in the puzzle for the Cyrillic words in the clues below.

Across

1. запад
5. автобус
7. Спасибо
9. десять
11. цирк
12. сегодня
13. тут
15. На помошь
16. хорошо
17. До свидания

Down

1. когда
2. восток
3. обед
4. театр
5. корпус
6. три
8. вчера
10. сто
14. плохо

Baba Yaga—A Russian Folktale

Use with page 26.

In a little house on the edge of the Forest, there once lived a Cat, a Sparrow, and a Brave Youth. One day the Cat and the Sparrow decided to go into the Forest to chop some wood. "We are going into the Forest to chop some wood," they told the Brave Youth. "If Baba Yaga comes to count the spoons, be very quiet. Don't say a word."

While they were gone into the Forest, Baba Yaga came to count the spoons. "This is the Cat's spoon. This is the Sparrow's spoon. And this is the Brave Youth's spoon," said Baba Yaga. The Brave Youth tried to remain quiet, but he could not restrain himself. "Baba Yaga, don't touch my spoon!" he cried.

Baba Yaga seized the Brave Youth and flew away on her broom. The Youth cried for help. "Cat, run! Sparrow, fly!" Hearing the Brave Youth, the Cat and the Sparrow rushed to his aid. The Cat scratched and the Sparrow pecked. Baba Yaga dropped the Youth and flew back to her home.

The next day, the Cat and the Sparrow returned to the Forest to chop some wood. "We are going even deeper into the Forest to chop some wood," they told the Brave Youth. "If Baba Yaga comes to count the spoons, don't say anything. We will not be able to rescue you today."

The Brave Youth sat down by the stove and waited. Soon Baba Yaga came into the house and began to count the spoons. "This is the Cat's spoon, this is the Sparrow's spoon, and this is the Brave Youth's spoon," she said. The Brave Youth was angry but did not say a word. Again, Baba Yaga counted the spoons. "This is the Cat's spoon, this is the Sparrow's spoon, and this is the Brave Youth's spoon." Again the Youth did not say a word.

Baba Yaga picked up the spoons for a third time and counted. "This is the Cat's spoon, this

is the Sparrow's spoon, and this is the Brave Youth's spoon." The Brave Youth could no longer restrain himself. "Baba Yaga, don't touch my spoon!"

Baba Yaga seized the Brave Youth and flew away on her broom. The Youth cried for help, but the Cat and the Sparrow could not hear him. Baba Yaga put the Brave Youth inside her hut and called for her daughter.

"Come make a fire in the stove and roast this Brave Youth for my supper tonight," she said.

So the daughter made a fire and told the Brave Youth to get in the pan. He quietly laid in the pan with one foot on the ceiling and one foot on the floor.

"Not like that," said the daughter.

"I don't know how to lay in the pan," said the Youth. "Show me how and I will do it."

So the daughter climbed in the pan to show the Brave Youth how to lie in it. The Youth quickly shoved the pan in the oven and roasted the daughter.

Baba Yaga—A Russian Folktale (Cont.)

Use with page 25.

When Baba Yaga returned, she smelled dinner roasting in the oven. "Ah! Now I am going to feast on the Brave Youth's bones!" she said.

"Feast yourself on your own daughter's bones," said the Youth hiding in the corner.

"Ah, you little cheat! You won't get away," said Baba Yaga. "Come out and lie in the pan."

So the Brave Youth came out and lay in the pan with one foot on the ceiling and the other on the floor.

"Not that way," said Baba Yaga.

"But I don't know how to lie in the pan," said the Youth. "Show me how and I will do it."

So Baba Yaga climbed in the pan. Quickly the Youth shoved her in the oven and roasted Baba Yaga. Then he ran home and told his friends, the Cat and the Sparrow, how he had defeated Baba Yaga.

1. Some believe this story was borrowed from Russia and retold as "Hansel and Gretel." How is it like "Hansel and Gretel"? How is it different? _____

_____

_____

2. Why did the Brave Youth tell Baba Yaga to leave his spoon alone? _____

_____

3. Are there situations when it is better to keep quiet? Explain. _____

_____

4. How did the Brave Youth defeat Baba Yaga? _____

_____

5. Russian folk tales have many stories about Baba Yaga. What other "bad" characters are common in fairy tales? _____

_____

6. "Little Red Riding Hood" also comes from Russia. How is it similar or different from "Baba Yaga and the Brave Youth"? _____

_____

Russian Proverbs

Russians have preserved some of their wisdom in the form of proverbs. Below are listed some of the proverbs. Read each proverb and write what each one means in the space provided.

1. Look after your clothes when they're spic and span, and after your honor when you're a young man.

   _____

   _____

2. A morsel always looks big in other people's hands.

   _____

   _____

3. There would be no going to the woods if one thought all the time about wolves.

   _____

   _____

4. You can't jump over your own head.

   _____

   _____

5. Hunger is rather a mean stepmother.

   _____

   _____

6. Things are as all right as soot is white.

   _____

   _____

7. There is yet powder in the powder horns.

   _____

   _____

8. Cat's cheers are mice's tears.

   _____

   _____

Russian Ballet–The Nutcracker

Use with page 29.

Ballet was brought to the Russian royal court in 1732. In the 1800s, famous choreographers from France and Italy helped ballet become a highly developed art form. Eventually, Russian composers and choreographers began to create their own ballets. The most famous and most often performed ballets were written by Peter Tchaikovsky. They are *Swan Lake* (1876), *The Sleeping Beauty* (1890), and *The Nutcracker* (1892).

Russian ballet is characterized by incredible grace and fantastic leaps. To better understand the grace and beauty of Russian Ballet, read the following story about *The Nutcracker*, and then watch a video of the ballet performance. The best example stars one of the greatest Russian dancers, Mikhail Baryshnikov.

The Nutcracker

One fine Christmas Eve, Clara and her family were having a wonderful party. There was a beautiful Christmas tree decorated with all the latest fashions. There was also lots of wonderful food.

"Merry Christmas," she said to each guest as they arrived. Each guest kissed Clara on the cheek and then went inside for dancing and presents.

The last to arrive was Clara's Godfather, Herr Drosselmeyer. He was a wonderful storyteller and some thought he could perform magic.

"Merry Christmas," he said as he handed her a present.

"Merry Christmas," she said. Then she opened the present to find a large wooden nutcracker. "He looks like a very brave soldier," she said.

"Ah, he is!" said Herr Drosselmeyer.

She was admiring her present when her little brother Fritz jumped from behind the couch and grabbed the Nutcracker. He laughed as he ran from Clara. Soon all the children were chasing Fritz. They were laughing and giggling until Fritz tripped and dropped the Nutcracker.

Clara rushed over to it and found that it had broken its jaw in the fall. Gently she picked it up and carried it to Herr Drosselmeyer.

"Why Clara," he said. "Don't you know that many brave soldiers are wounded in battle?" He took out his handkerchief and tied it around the Nutcracker's broken jaw. "There. This kerchief will be his bandage and you shall be his nurse."

Clara carefully carried the wounded Nutcracker up to her bed and cared for it. Then she curled up and fell asleep with the Nutcracker still in her arms.

While she was sleeping, Herr Drosselmeyer came into the room. He untied the handkerchief and waved it over Clara and the Nutcracker. Suddenly, the Nutcracker turned into a handsome prince. He watched her lovingly as he stood guard over her through the night.

Clara heard a noise and woke up. She screamed when she saw her Nutcracker prince battling huge mice. He was fighting with one mouse that had a golden crown on its head.

Russian Ballet–The Nutcracker (Cont.)

Use with page 28.

"Leave the Nutcracker alone!" she cried. She jumped up and pulled on the mouse's tail. The mouse was so startled that it ran away. Seeing their leader gone, the other mice scattered.

"Thank you for your help," said the prince in a deep, rich voice. Then he picked up the crown that the mouse had dropped and placed it on Clara's head. As soon as he did, Clara's nightgown turned into a beautiful dress that sparkled in the moonlight.

"Please, come to my kingdom in the Land of Sweets where my friends can also thank you," said the prince. Together they stepped out into the night. The fresh, falling snow whirled around them in a fluffy, white dance, carrying them to the Land of Sweets.

Everyone living in the Land of Sweets was named after something delicious. All were excited when the prince told them how Clara had saved him from the huge mice. They carried the prince and Clara to their thrones and then performed beautiful dances for them.

First came the peppermint candy canes, wearing red and white stripes. Then a dainty Sugar Plum Fairy danced with a soldier.

The Dew Drop Fairy gracefully pirouetted, followed by several tiny angels with miniature wings. As the flowers danced, they waved their tiny petals at the royal couple. However, Clara's favorite dancer was Mother Ginger, who hid six pixie children beneath her large skirt.

When all the dancers had finished, Clara and the prince rose to their feet and applauded them. "We should go now," said the prince. "But every Christmas Eve we will return to the Land of Sweets."

Then they climbed into a sleigh drawn by two reindeer. They waved to all their new friends and flew off into the early morning sky. Soon they were home, where they enjoyed a very Merry Christmas.

Music–Peter and the Wolf

Use with page 31.

In the late 19th century, Russian composers were known for creating magnificent music. These composers included Mikhail Glinka, Alexandr Borodin, Modest Mussorgsky, Nikolai Rimsky-Korsakov, and Peter Tchaikovsky. Modern composers include Igor Stravinsky, Sergei Prokofiev, and Dimitri Shostakovich. Many of the symphonies, ballets, and operas incorporate Russian folk songs and traditional dances.

One symphonic fairy tale is *Peter and the Wolf* by Sergei Prokofiev. It is unique because each of the instruments of the orchestra is featured separately. It is a good opportunity to gain a real sense of what each instrument sounds like. Also, each of the characters in the story is represented by a separate melody. So it is fairly easy to follow the story by listening to the music.

Read the story of *Peter and the Wolf*. Then listen to the symphony. Can you understand the story by listening to the music? Finally, watch the Disney cartoon of *Peter and the Wolf*. Describe how literature, music, and art were combined to make this cartoon.

Peter and the Wolf

Far up in northern Russia on the edge of the forest lived a boy named Peter and his grandfather. Peter loved to roam through the forest and had made many animal friends. Every winter, grandfather warned Peter not to go into the forest. "Food is scarce in the winter," he said. "That's when the wolves are hungry enough to hunt little boys. You must wait until you are old enough to hunt them."

Peter was sure he was old enough to hunt. He was not afraid, and he was certainly more clever than a wolf. So he waited until grandfather was asleep. Then he took his wooden gun and a long coil of rope and headed into the woods to hunt wolves.

Peter walked very carefully. He was searching for signs of the wolf. "Hello," said a little voice. Peter jumped at the sound, but it was only his friend Sasha, a little bird. "Where are you going?" she asked.

"I'm hunting the wolf," said Peter.

"May I come, too?" asked Sasha.

Peter nodded and off they went. Before long they ran into two other friends. Sonia the duck and Ivan the cat both wanted to help Peter hunt the wolf. Sasha was not happy that Ivan was going along because cats like to eat small birds. But Peter assured Sasha that Ivan would behave.

Quietly, the small group of hunters searched for signs of the wolf. Suddenly, there was a noise behind them. They whirled around and stood face to face with the wolf. Peter leaped straight up and grabbed a branch. Ivan ran up the tree, and Sasha flew out of the way. However, Sonia was not so lucky. The wolf pounced on her before she could move.

"Ivan!" cried Peter. "I have an idea."

Music–Peter and the Wolf (Cont.)

Use with page 30.

Peter lowered his rope carefully toward the wolf. Ivan scurried down the tree and looped the rope over the wolf's tail. Then Peter pulled with all his strength. Ivan ran back up the tree to help him. Soon they pulled the wolf right off his feet.

"Sasha! Go get some help," said Peter.

Sasha flew off. She found a group of hunters not far away. She darted at them and flew in circles.

"Look at that bird," said one of the hunters. "I think she is trying to tell us something."

"Let's follow her and find out," said another. So they followed Sasha back to where Peter and Ivan were. When they arrived, they found the wolf all tied up and hanging from a branch.

"Look at that," said the hunters. "Peter has captured the wolf!"

As they got ready to carry the wolf back to town, a cloud of feathers burst from under a log. Sonia had been trapped there when the wolf pounced on her. She was glad to be free. She was even happier to see that Peter caught the wolf.

When they marched into town, all the people cheered. They were proud of Peter. And grandfather was proudest of all.

Have a Feast!

Use with page 33.

Sibirskije Peljmeni (Siberian Ravioli)

3 cups flour
1¼ tsp. salt
2 eggs, slightly beaten
3 tbs. water, ice-cold
1 lb. ground beef, cooked
1 med. onion, finely chopped
¼ tsp. pepper

1 egg yolk, beaten
4 cups chicken stock
3 cups beef stock
chopped fresh dill
sliced carrots
onion rings

1. Stir flour and ¼ tsp. salt.
2. Stir in 2 eggs and 6–8 tbs. water.
3. Wrap in plastic wrap and let stand for 20 min.
4. Knead dough until smooth and set aside.
5. To make filling, in a large bowl combine beef, onion, 3 tbs. ice-cold water, 1 tsp. salt, and ¼ tsp. pepper.
6. Divide dough into 4 equal pieces.
7. Roll out each piece until 1/16 inch thick.
8. Cut dough into 2" circles.
9. Brush edges of dough with egg yolk.
10. Place ½ tsp. filling in each circle and fold over.
11. Crimp edges with a fork and let stand for 10 min.
12. Pour beef and chicken broth into a large pot.
13. Add sliced carrots and onion rings to broth and bring to a boil.
14. Add ravioli a few at a time while boiling.
15. Reduce heat and simmer for 10 min.

Serve in bowls and garnish with dill.

Kulebjaka (Cabbage Pastie)

3 tbs. butter

3 onions, finely chopped

2 lbs. cabbage, shredded and
    blanched 5 min. in water

1 cup water

3 hard-boiled eggs, chopped

3 tbs. chopped dill

2 tbs. chopped parsley

white pepper

$^1/_4$ tsp. sugar

Pastry:

$^3/_4$ cup butter, chilled

2 tbs. butter, chilled

2–$^3/_4$ cups flour

6 tbs. sour cream

1 egg, beaten

1 egg yolk, beaten

To Make Filling:

1. Preheat oven to 350°.
2. Melt butter in a casserole dish.
3. Add onions and saute until golden brown.
4. Add blanched cabbage and water.
5. Cover and bake 30–40 min.
6. When cabbage is tender, drain and cool.
7. Stir in hard-boiled eggs, dill, parsley, salt, white pepper, and sugar.

To Make Pastry:

1. Put flour in a medium bowl.
2. Use a fork to cut in butter.
3. Stir in sour cream and whole egg.
4. Shape into a ball and refrigerate 15 min.

To Make Kulebjaka:

1. Roll out $^1/_2$ of chilled pastry into an oval $^1/_4$" thick.
2. Place on a greased baking sheet.
3. Roll out remaining pastry into a slightly larger oval.
4. Heat oven to 425°.
5. Spoon filling into smaller pastry.
6. Cover with larger pastry and fold bottom edge over top edge.
7. Pinch together to seal edges.
8. Cut a hole in the top of the pastry.
9. Brush with egg yolk and refrigerate 15 min.
10. Bake 30 min. until golden brown.

Makes 8-10 servings

Conquest of Space

In 1957, the USSR launched "Sputnik." It was the first satellite ever put into orbit. America was shocked. The Soviets were first into space!

This single fact altered everything—from our approach to education to worrying about "spies in the skies." In fact, President Kennedy declared the U.S.'s intention to land on the moon in his inaugeral address of 1961.

List of Space Firsts:

October 4, 1957 — 1st satellite in space
- "Sputnik I" (U.S.S.R.)

November 3, 1957 — 1st animal in space
- Laika was a female dog that lived about one week until her oxygen ran out (U.S.S.R.)

April 12, 1961 — 1st man in space
- Yuri Gagarin on "Vostok I" (U.S.S.R.)

June 16–19, 1963 — 1st woman in space
- Valentina Tereshkova on "Vostok VI" (U.S.S.R.)

March 18, 1965 — 1st man to walk in space
- Aleksei Leonov (U.S.S.R.)

May 5, 1961 — 1st American in space
- Alan Shepard (U.S.)

February 20, 1962 — 1st American to orbit the earth
- John Glenn, Jr. (U.S.)

July 20, 1969 — 1st man on the moon
- Neil Armstrong (U.S.)

1971 — 1st manned space station
- Salyut I (U.S.S.R.)

• Draw an illustration of one of the first satellites.

The Taiga

The Taiga is the largest forest in the world! It comprises one-third of the world's forestland. It covers most of eastern Russia.

Fact: Lumbering rights have been sold to other countries for the next 30 years.

Fact: These countries have been clear-cutting the forest in an attempt to harvest as much lumber as possible.

Fact: These countries are not replanting the trees they are harvesting.

Fact: The Taiga is home to hundreds of species of animals. Some, like the Siberian tiger, are found nowhere else in the world.

Fact: To clear-cut a forest means to harvest all the trees regardless of size or quality.

Fact: Clear-cutting destroys animal habitat.

Fact: Loss of animal habitat results in moving and usually killing the animals. Some species cannot live anywhere else, so they become extinct. Remember, extinction is permanent.

Fact: Clear-cutting significantly raises the risk of forest fires.

Fact: Clear-cutting allows the rain to wash away precious topsoil and further damage the environment through erosion.

Fact: The forest cannot regrow if there are no trees left to provide the seeds.

Fact: Select-cutting is more expensive than clear-cutting.

Fact: Select cutting takes only the best lumber and leaves the rest of the forest for the animals and future generations.

Fact: Clear-cutting makes more profit but ruins the environment for everyone.

1. Which facts are most important to you? Why? _____

_____

_____

_____

_____

2. Russia needs to sell lumber. How can they do it so everyone wins? _____

_____

_____

_____

_____

Feline Skeleton

Unscramble the names of some of the bones of a cat skeleton. Not all names will be used.

1. **bojanews** _____
2. **wrtsi** _____
3. **ariuds** _____
4. **paceekn** _____
5. **leeh** _____
6. **oet senbo** _____
7. **sbir** _____

8. **ulbafi** _____
9. **ibiat** _____
10. **tatrmealsas** _____
11. **urmfe** _____
12. **lulks** _____
13. **elpsiv** _____

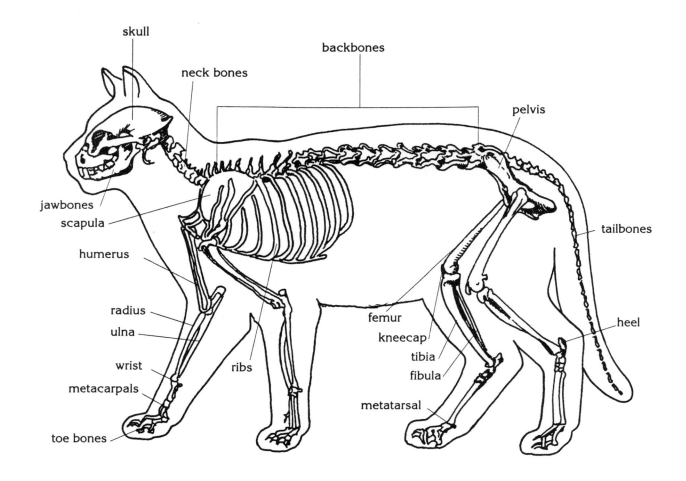

Siberian Tiger Facts

Scientific Name: *Panthera tigris altaica*

Also known as the Amur Tiger, and the Manchurian Tiger

Average Size: 12–13 feet long from nose to tail; about 3 feet tall at the shoulder; they are the largest of all the species of tigers and the biggest cat in the world. Average Weight: females are up to 400 pounds; males are up to 700 pounds.

Habitat: The forests of the Sikhote-Alin Mtns. in far eastern Russia; temperatures often reach far below 0° Fahrenheit.

Appearance: They are covered with very thick fur that keeps them warm in sub-zero temperatures; their feet are covered with thick fur to allow them to walk comfortably in the snow; they have been hunted extensively for the beauty of their fur.

Unique Features: Tigers are the only cats found in the wild with stripes; tigers cannot purr, they can only roar.

Siberian tigers do not eat humans. In fact, they are very shy. It is the rare person who even glimpses one; they quickly hide from people.

Status: The Siberian tiger was hunted almost to extinction in the early 1900s. In 1947, the U.S.S.R. strictly protected them. By 1991 there were 300–500 left in the wild. With the fall of the U.S.S.R., hunting resumed. Within three years about 100 tigers were killed illegally and sold on the black market.

— **Activity** —

Draw a realistic illustration of a Siberian tiger in its habitat.

Tiger Extinction

The majestic tiger is threatened by a loss of habitat and poaching. There are now only 5,000–7,500 tigers left on the earth. That is a loss of roughly 95% of the tiger population during this century alone!

Bengal Tiger: There were around 3,700 of these tigers left in India. Even though they are protected in wildlife preserves, they suffered a 35% loss between 1989 and 1992.

South China Tiger: They were declared a national pest by Mao Tse Tung. He ordered them to be hunted everywhere. Today there are only 30–80 left in the wild.

Bali Tiger: This tiger was hunted to extinction in the 1940s.

Sumatran Tiger: There are now less than 650 left roaming southeast India.

Indo-Chinese Tiger: This tiger roams the lower slopes of the Himilayan Mountains in northern India. Its inhospitable habitat has not protected it from humans. There are between 1,000 and 1,700 left in the wild.

Caspian Tiger: Hunted to extinction in the 1970s.

Javan Tiger: Hunted to extinction in the 1980s.

Siberian Tiger: The largest of all cats used to roam over most of northern China and Korea. They were hunted to extinction everywhere except far eastern Russia. There are less than 300 remaining in the forest. Between 80–96 were killed in 1993 alone! If poaching is not stopped, they will become extinct by the year 2000.

— **Activity** —

Write a story in which you are part of a tiger rescue team that found the orphaned cub and are putting it in a preserve. Will it survive?

To Hunt or Not to Hunt

You live in Vladivostok, Russia. You work very hard and earn the average wage of $500 a year. That's the equivalent of 24¢ an hour! A man asks if you would like to earn some extra money by killing a tiger. Below is a summary of what he offers.

Tiger Skin $10,000

Whiskers (believed to give strength and long life) $1,000

Eyes (believed to calm convulsions) $1,000

Bones (believed to cure rheumatism) $3,000

What would you do? Why?

_____

_____

_____

_____

_____

_____

_____

_____

_____

Five Kinds of Life

Use with page 41.

There are five types of life on earth. They are listed in the box below. Each depends on another to live. If one kind of life is eliminated, it hurts all the others. Label each picture with the type of life it is.

1. **Producer:**
   Eat—sunlight, carbon dioxide and soil
   Feed—primary consumers and decomposers
   Examples — grass, herbs

2. **Primary Consumer:**
   Eat—grass and oxygen
   Feed—secondary consumers, scavengers,
          decomposers, producers (oxygen)
   Examples — rabbits, deer

3. **Secondary Consumer:**
   Eat—primary consumers and oxygen
   Feed—scavengers, decomposers, producers (oxygen)
   Examples—tigers, wolves

4. **Scavenger:**
   Eat—primary consumers,
          secondary consumers, and oxygen
   Feed—decomposers and producers (oxygen)
   Examples—vultures, crows

5. **Decomposer:**
   Eat—dead producers, dead primary consumers,
          dead secondary consumers, dead scavengers
   Feed—soil and producers
   Examples—mushrooms, bacteria

The Circle of Life

Identify the following forms of life as either producers, primary consumers, secondary consumers, scavengers, or decomposers. Then write their names on the *Circle of Life* below.

Tiger _____ Snow Leopard _____

Porcupine _____ Wild Boar _____

Bacteria _____ Pine Tree _____

Eagle _____ Vulture _____

Grass _____ Mouse _____

Mushroom _____ Raven _____

Elk _____

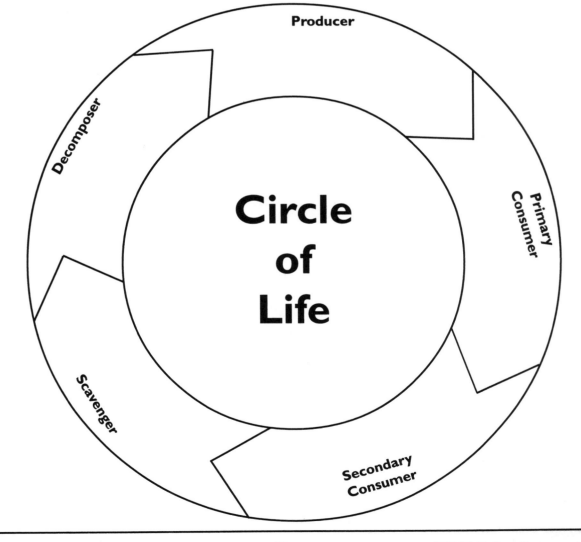

Earth Alert Journal

Create an *EARTH ALERT!* journal. Use this form to record any situations that endanger the environment. Every time an article is found in a newspaper, magazine, or even on television, record the facts on the *Earth Alert!* form. Collect all the reports in a notebook/journal that the entire class can share.

EARTH ALERT!

Name:	Date:

Endangered Location:

Source of Information:

Main Problem:

Causes:

1.

2.

3.

4.

Secondary Problems:

1.

2.

3.

4.

Possible Solutions:

1.

2.

3.

4.

Global Warming

Is the world getting warmer? Inquiring minds want to know!

According to the greenhouse effect theory, increased levels of carbon dioxide and CFCs (chlorofluorocarbons) in the atmosphere create a shield over the earth. When the sun shines on the earth, it warms the surface. Normally, much of the heat escapes back into space at night. However, the carbon dioxide shield reflects some of the heat back to the earth at night. So the world does not cool off as it should but gradually gets warmer over the years.

The main concern is that the polar ice caps will melt and flood the coastlines. Weather patterns could also change dramatically.

Carbon dioxide levels are increasing because factories burn fossil fuels and forests are being cut down.

1. Discover how cutting down forests increases carbon dioxide levels.

2. Discover how burning fossil fuels increases carbon dioxide levels.

3. What are CFCs and how do they work?

4. Check with your local weather station (which may be affiliated with a local radio or TV station). Obtain records of average temperatures for the last 100 years. See if the earth is getting warmer.

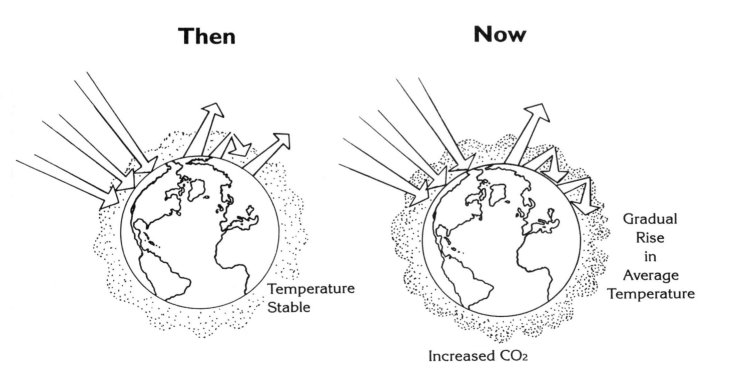

Then

Now

Temperature Stable

Gradual Rise in Average Temperature

Increased CO_2

Smog

Smog is a low cloud of ozone. The ozone layer around the earth is needed to prevent many of the sun's harmful rays from causing skin cancer. However, when humans breathe ozone, it breaks down tissue and attacks the respiratory system. It reduces lung capacity and causes severe coughing, shortness of breath, chest pain, and congestion.

Smog is caused by the release of sulfur dioxide and nitrous oxides from factories and power plants. It is also caused by the release of carbon monoxide and nitrous oxides from automobiles.

Over 1,000 cities in Russia have five times the permitted levels of smog. Ten cities have 100 times the allowed concentrations of these toxic particles in the air. The air in Petrograd (Leningrad) is reported to be so bad that one out of three residents suffer some respiratory disease.

—— Activity ——

Examine your city (or a city near you) to discover smog levels. Many cities have air quality reports given regularly over the radio.

Other Animals of Russia

Lynx:
Poachers hunt for skins and traditional medicine.

Amur Goral Goats:
In Siberia's Lhazovsky Reserve, hunters blast these rare mammals off the cliffs with automatic weapons.

Snow Leopards:
These beautiful creatures are hunted for many of the same reasons as is the Siberian tiger.

Saiga Antelope:
As rhino horn becomes scarce, the Saiga male is being hunted for its horns as a rhino horn substitute in the traditional medicine market. Saiga horn sells for $350–$500 per kilo.

Amur Leopards:
As the Siberian tiger becomes rare, the Amur leopard is being substituted to fill the demands of the traditional medicine market.

Marco Polo Sheep:
These animals are also being hunted for their horns. The traditional medicine market pays high prices for their horns.

Siberian Ibex:
This animal is valued for its horns as well as for its beautiful fur.

Markhors:
The magnificent five-foot horns of this goat sell for as much as $10,000 on the traditional medicine market. There are currently only 400 left in the world and authorities have no plans to protect the animal.

Himalayan Black Bear:
These bears are being hunted in great numbers for their gallbladders. On the traditional medicine market, a bear gallbladder sells for as much as $3,000.

— **Activity** —

Choose one of the above animals on which to write a report. Include an illustration with your report.

The Tiger Umbrella

Tigers usually live alone in large territories which they mark. If the Russian government protects the Siberian tiger, it will have to set aside vast tracts of forest. However, this action will also protect a host of other animals that share the same forest. Environmentalists call this an umbrella. In other words, what protects the tiger will protect the rest of the forest biome.

What other species are being focused on in the world to produce umbrellas? Hint: Pandas and spotted owls are two examples.

Fill in the tiger mobile below with names of other animals of Russia to illustrate how an umbrella may protect other animals.

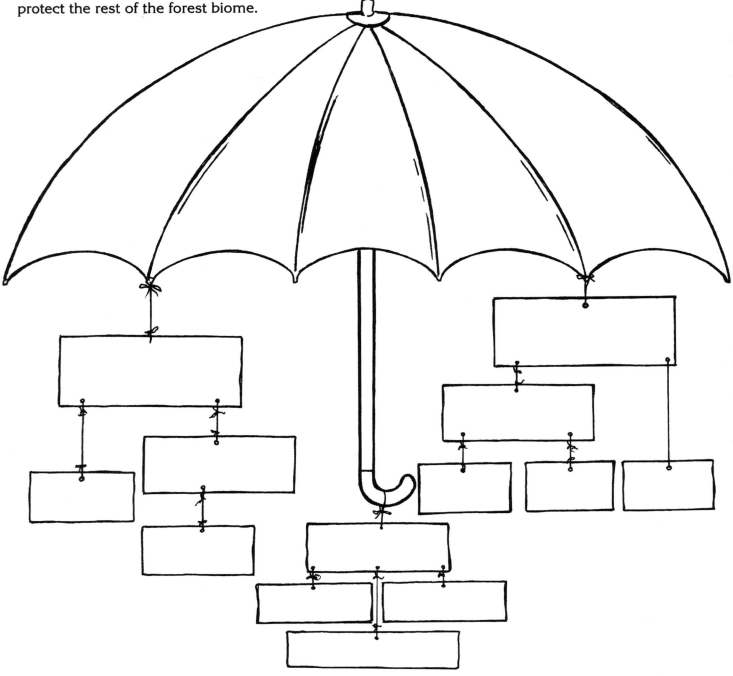

Answer Key

Page 5

13	Aral Sea
12	Caspian Sea
8	Barents Sea
6	Black Sea
9	White Sea
19	Bering Sea
5	Sea of Azov
23	Sea of Japan
20	Sea of Okhotsk
11	Lake Ladoga
15	Lake Baikal
10	Gulf of Finland
18	Bering Strait
4	Dnepr River
3	Volga River
24	Yenisey River
14	Ob River
16	Lena River
17	Amur River
2	Ural Mtns.
7	Caucasus Mtns.
1	Arctic Circle
21	Sakhalin Island
22	Kuril Islands

Page 6

1. Sweden
2. China
3. Belarus
4. Georgia
5. Japan
6. Turkey
7. Uzbekistan
8. Ukraine
9. Latvia
10. Estonia
11. Iran
12. Turkmenistan
13. Kyrgyzstan
14. Poland
15. Kazakstan
16. Russia

Page 7

Page 8

1. 76%
2. 55%
3. 56%
4. 39%
5. 61%
6. 56%
7. 45%
8. 71%
9. 96%
10. 82%
11. Answers will vary.

Page 9

1. Yekaterinburg   2:00 P.M.
   Novosibirsk   4:00 P.M.
   Yakutsk   5:00 P.M.
2. Answers will vary. The varying time zones create many difficulties.

Page 17

1. Extremely. A means of transporting supplies is essential.
2. Answers will vary.
3. Answers will vary. Only local product.
4. 4,971 miles
   (8,000 km x 0.62137 mile)
5. 47.6 km per hour
6. Answers will vary.
7. Answers will vary.

Answer Key

Page 24

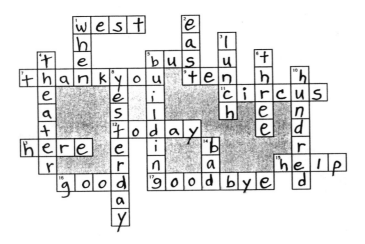

Page 41

Tiger = Secondary Consumer

Porcupine = Primary Consumer

Bacteria = Decomposer

Eagle = Secondary Consumer

Grass = Producer

Mushroom = Decomposer

Elk = Primary Consumer

Snow Leopard = Secondary Consumer

Wild Boar = Primary Consumer

Pine Tree = Producer

Vulture = Scavenger

Mouse = Primary Consumer

Raven = Scavenger

Page 36

1. jawbones
2. wrist
3. radius
4. kneecap
5. heel
6. toe bones
7. ribs
8. fibula
9. tibia
10. metatarsal
11. femur
12. skull
13. pelvis

Page 40

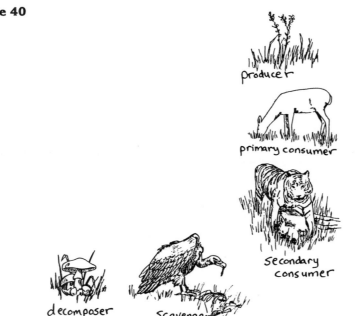

producer

primary consumer

secondary consumer

decomposer

scavenger